the harbour, too. We'll all cross in safety,

blue, The best trains started it, Brave men

the harbour, too. We'll all cross in safety, And busy trains

ies of blue, The best trains started it, Brave men wrought it,

Bridge of our Dreams Come True.

The Sydney Harbour Bridge

75 Fascinating Facts

To Penny, Anna and Anthony

The Sydney Harbour Bridge

75 Fascinating Facts

Peter Luck

We're building a bridge in Sydney
Over the harbour, too.
We'll all cross in safety,
And busy trains pass through.
A wonderful thing of beauty,
Arching the skies of blue,
The best brains started it,
Brave men wrought it,
Bridge of our Dreams Come True.

– popular song

by Peter Luck

Seventy-five illustrated factual vignettes commemorating
Australia's triumphant engineering feat during the Great
Depression—the building of the Sydney Harbour Bridge,
which opened on March 19, 1932.

The Sydney Harbour Bridge, while appearing curved, is in fact made of only straight pieces of steel.

Originally described as "the eighth wonder of the world", the Bridge is affectionately known to Sydneysiders as "the coat hanger".

The engineer of the Bridge, John Job Crew Bradfield, had such
a large head that medical experts once measured it to test contemporary
theories about brain size and intelligence.

Two Australian icons only metres from where the First Fleet landed in 1788.

Thirty-nine people jumped from the Bridge in the first year of its existence (three survived), prompting authorities to erect a protective fence.

Rescue workers save another would-be suicide from a watery grave.

The Bridge is painted on the inside as well as on the outside. A total of 272,000 litres of Berger paint was used in the first three coats.

Painters now wear more safety and protective gear than did this vintage worker.

During the Depression the Bridge was called "the Iron Lung" because of the number of workers it kept employed and fed.

Jim Barbour, a riveter on the Bridge, saw one of his mates fall to his death.

Eight hundred houses were demolished to make way for the Bridge and their owners received no compensation. However, the ferry company was compensated for the demolition of the Milsons Point arcade.

The progress of the Bridge monopolised ferry boat conversation for six years.

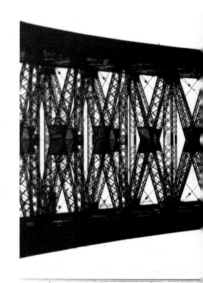

Detonator positions were marked on the Bridge to blow it up if the Japanese or Germans had successfully invaded Sydney during World War II.

Friendly flyover – Bridge climbers watch RAAF Roulettes in action.

Unlike the Golden Gate Bridge in San Francisco, which had safety nets to catch falling workers ("The Half Way to Hell Club"), Sydney Harbour Bridge had no such nets and eight men fell to their deaths – the first on March 6, 1930. Eight others were killed on the project.

Stairway to heaven.

Worker Vince Kelly fell 45 metres (150 feet) from the Bridge and survived. He knew he had to hit the water feet first; nevertheless, the uppers of his boots were reportedly pushed up to his thighs. He broke three ribs when he hit the water – an impact which sent spray 27 metres (90 feet) into the air. Kelly (above right) was back at work after 17 days and was welcomed by minister for works, Davidson. He died in 1982.

A promotional model for the Dutch airline KLM passes under the Bridge. In 1942 some of the airline's DC aircraft were actually flown under the Bridge.

When it was built, the Sydney Harbour Bridge was the largest steel arch in the world. A similar structure, the Bayonne (Kill van Kull) Bridge which opened in New York in 1931, was 60 centimetres longer but half as wide and half as heavy.

The Bridge in 1930 – the creeper cranes could climb half the arch in a week.

The last of six million rivets on the Bridge was placed in the top of the arch on the eastern side. The largest rivet weighed 3.5 kilograms.

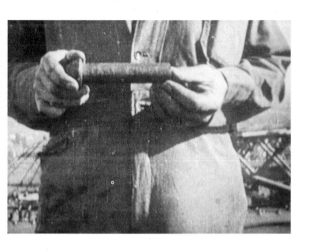

In 1791 Dr Erasmus Darwin, grandfather of Charles Darwin, penned these prophetic words about Sydney, "There the proud arch, Colossus-like, Bestride yon' glittering streams and bound the chafing tide".

On Golden Pond – twilight falls over the Opera House, Bridge and Mrs Macquarie's Point.

About half the population of Sydney, which was
1.2 million at the time, turned out for the opening
of the Bridge on March 19, 1932.

"People as far as the eye can see", said the newsreel commentator.

The first plans for a bridge were proposed by the convict architect Francis Greenway in 1815. Sir Henry Parkes allocated money for the building of a harbour bridge in 1881 but lost the following election. He campaigned with the slogan: "Now, who will stand at my right hand, and build a bridge with me?" Plans for a harbour bridge were controversial and were the subject of two Royal Commissions in the 1890s and early 1900s.

Replica of Captain Bligh's ship Bounty *heading west.*

The RSL wanted to name the Harbour Bridge the "Anzac Bridge" and proposed to have the "rising sun" badge motif at the top of the arch.

It would be a lifetime before Sydney would get another harbour crossing of the magnitude of the Sydney Harbour Bridge. The Anzac Bridge opened on December 2, 1995.

The first car to cross the Bridge, a Model A Ford, contained John Bradfield and his family and was driven by Bradfield's youngest son, Stan. The first man to walk from shore to shore on the Harbour Bridge was James Holt, a worker.

Peak hour, 1932.

When a worker died on the Bridge his fellow workers gave half a day's pay to the widow. Only two of the men who died were married and their dependants received compensation ranging from $800 to $1600, with $50 for each dependant child. Workers without dependants were awarded $40 burial expenses only.

Sydney's historic Garrison Church was built in 1840 as a place for soldiers to worship.

The Bridge's arch weighs 39,006 tonnes and the rivets alone weigh 3,200 tonnes. During construction more than 100,000 rivets were regarded as faulty by the inspectors and had to be cut out and replaced.

The Bridge builders Dorman Long submitted designs with and without pylons.

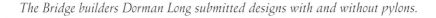

The Bridge's towers are purely decorative and contain 40,000 pieces of granite and 95,000 cubic metres of concrete.

As many as 1,000 visitors climb to the top of the bridge each day.

The original toll on the Bridge – 6d,
(sixpence, the equivalent of five cents)
for driver plus 3d for any other adult in
the car and a penny for children (the
toll to be paid both ways) – was much
more than $3 in today's money. Toll
for a horse and rider was 3d, loose
stock 2d, sheep and pigs 1d per head,
3d for a bicycle.

For whom the Bridge tolls – southern approach.

To commemorate the closing of the arch, two flags were flown – the Union Jack on one creeper crane and the Australian Ensign on the other.

Almost there – the Bridge in 1930, photographed from Balmain.

CHORUS from the March
Sydney Harbour Bridge

Words and Music by
R. H. McANALLY

(M.M. ♩. = 120)

1. Might - - y work of man ____ triumphant ris - es o'er the
2. Sci - - ence and great skill ____ u-nit-ed work ____ and faithful

Har - - bour. Won - drous and grand it stands Monarch o - ver

Without any protection for their hearing, many of the boilermakers and iron workers on the Bridge went deaf.

The Bridge inspired hundreds of tributes in music, literature and art.

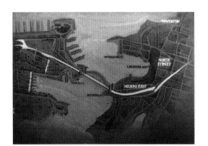

The loan money for the Bridge ran out a number of times and construction on the approaches had to cease.

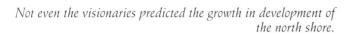

Not even the visionaries predicted the growth in development of the north shore.

The first words spoken after the Bridge's arch was joined were by Director of Construction, Lawrence Ennis, who said, "Well boys that's that ... and thank God she's home".

"Eight and three quarter inches to go" ... Ennis and Bradfield, August 1930.

In the first few years of the Bridge there were no toll booths so toll collectors stood in the open air.

What did they do when it rained?

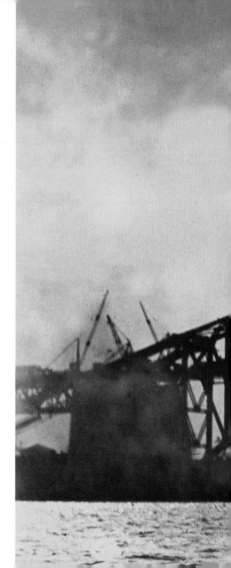

About 80 per cent of the steel in the Bridge came from England, including all the silicon steel for the arch. The remaining 20 per cent was Australian-made.

The massive steel arch still only weighs about half as much as some of the largest ships that pass beneath it.

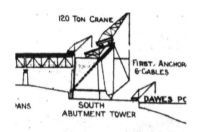

The weight of the Bridge is carried on just four bearing pins only 37centimetres in diameter. The bearings were manufactured in England and each weighs more than 300 tonnes.

Hinge – southern abutment. Note the size of the pin that supports the Bridge.

5
26.5.25

Alfred Edmonds, a 56-year-old labourer, had his thumb crushed while packing stones at North Sydney and died of tetanus 11 days later. Another worker, whose overalls were caught in a drill, lost a testicle.

The Bridge from railway shunting yards, White Bay, Rozelle.

The two hinged half-arches were held up by scores of steel cables which passed through horseshoe-shaped tunnels dug at each end of the Bridge. The wires were slackened off to allow the two ends to meet in August, 1930.

The Bridge dominated Circular Quay, originally called Semi-Circular Quay.

The Bridge was originally painted from end to end but these days it's just
a constant game of touch up.

Over the years Bridge authorities have resisted a number of representations
to change its colour, even to gold.

The maximum number of workers employed on the Bridge was 1654.

Bridge workers in 1932 – a surprising number were still around for a 50th anniversary reunion at the Sydney Town Hall.

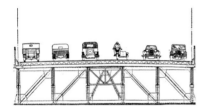

In 1932, when motorists began to use the Bridge as a "speedway", a white line was painted down the middle to create two lanes.

Opening day celebrated progress from Cobb and Co to motor coach.

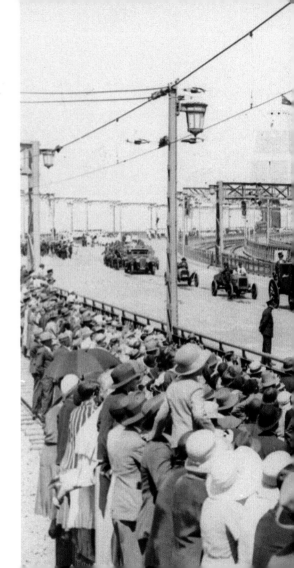

In 1934, about 12,000 vehicles crossed the Bridge each day. By the 1980s this figure had risen to almost 160,000.

A motley collection of Depression era jalopies, flivvers and T-Model Fords queues for the first drive across the Bridge on opening day.

Work began on the Bridge on April 18, 1923 although the turning of the first sod did not take place until July. The original estimate was around four million pounds ($8 million) and the final cost all up, including the approaches, was almost ten million pounds.

Luna Park now resides on the site of the factories temporarily erected to make many of the Bridge's steel components.

To stress test the Bridge, 92 steam engines were driven onto the tracks. If the experiment had failed we would have lost half of the NSW Railways as well as the bridge.

Sign of the times – the Bridge now has only one rail track.

The ribbon to open the Bridge was cut twice. The first time was by Irishman, Captain Francis de Groot a member of an extreme right-wing group called The New Guard. He slashed the ribbon with his sword in a protest against the opening ceremony not being performed by the king.

De Groot rampant. Sydney was shocked by his dramatic stunt and the prime minister, Joe Lyons, was depressed but the prankster had many supporters.

The ribbon was restored and then cut again with the official scissors by the premier of the day, Jack Lang. De Groot took his sword back to Ireland where it was rediscovered 75 years later and returned to Australia.

The ceremonial scissors, designed by Van Veinberg and inlaid with spectacular opals, now reside in the NSW Parliament House.

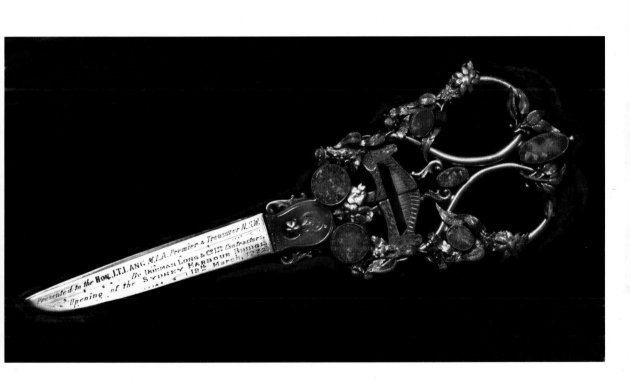

Presented to the Hon. J.T. LANG, M.L.A. Premier & Treasurer N.S.W.
By Dorman Long & Co Ltd Contractors;
Opening of the SYDNEY HARBOUR BRIDGE
19th March, 1932

The speed limit on the Bridge was raised from 60 to 70 kilometres per hour in 1991.

Traffic viewed from the base of the south-east pylon where the climb of the arch begins.

More than half a million people walked across the Bridge on its 50th birthday in 1982.

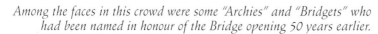

Among the faces in this crowd were some "Archies" and "Bridgets" who had been named in honour of the Bridge opening 50 years earlier.

Sydneysiders used to boast they were "three 'ours ahead of Melbourne....
'Our Bradman, 'our Bradfield and 'our Bridge."

A hugely popular poster by the celebrated designer, Douglas Annand.

SYDNEY BRIDGE

MARCH 19th 1932 **CELEBRATIONS** **BE THERE!**

Twenty-four thermometers were used
to measure the temperature on the
arch before it was joined at 10 pm on
a cool evening in August 1930. The
Bridge parted once briefly before
it was rejoined forever.

Messrs Ennis, Bradfield and Hipwell inspect the
imminent joining procedures –
note the oven to heat rivets at the left.

The first female toll collectors were introduced to the Bridge in 1979.

John D. Moore (1888–1958) Sydney Harbour *1936, oil on canvas, 91.5 cm x 122.5 cm, Art Gallery of NSW.*

The Bridge span measures 503 metres from pylon to pylon compared with the 1,280 metres of the Golden Gate Bridge in San Francisco.

The Bridge has outlasted some other landmarks which once impressed Sydneysiders so much, such as the battleship HMAS Australia *and the T&G building.*

Bridge 1650 Ft wide Between Pylons

H.M.A.S. Australia 600 Ft

Randwick Straight Just over two Furlongs

Melbourne Express 506 Ft

Tram 47.8 in

Coogee Pier 650 Ft

435 Ft to top of Arch

Sydney G.P.O. 210 Ft to flag Pole

Nelson's Column 145 Ft

Grace Bros Building 220 Ft High

T&G Building 222 Ft High

St Paul's Cathedral (LONDON) 404 Ft High

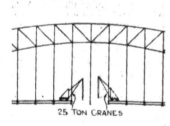

25 TON CRANES

The company which won the tender for the Bridge, Dorman Long of Middlesborough, England, put in seven tenders in all. Design number three was chosen.

The tenders show that almost a sixth of the cost of the Bridge was in the purely decorative pylons.

DORMAN LONG & CO. LTD.

TENDERS FOR AN ARCH BRIDGE

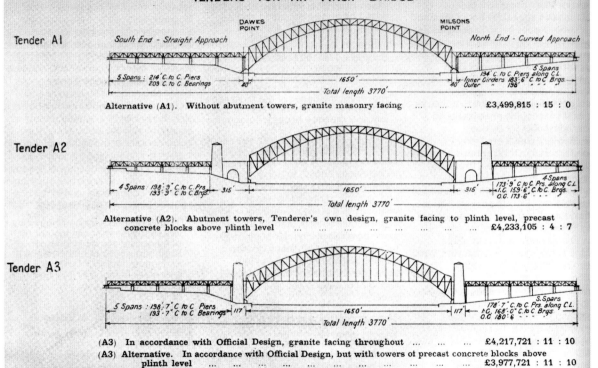

Tender A1

South End - Straight Approach

DAWES POINT

MILSONS POINT

North End - Curved Approach

5 Spans : 214' C. to C. Piers
209' C. to C. Bearings

40'

1650'

194' C. to C. Piers along C.L.
Inner Girders 183' 6" C. to C. Brgs.
Outer " 198' " " "

40'

5 Spans

Total length 3770'

Alternative (A1). Without abutment towers, granite masonry facing ... ... £3,499,815 : 15 : 0

Tender A2

4 Spans : 198' 9" C. to C. Prs.
193' 3" C. to C. Brgs.

315'

1650'

315'

173' 9" C. to C. Prs. along C.L.
I.G. 159' 6" C. to C. Brgs.
O.G. 173' 6" " " "

4 Spans

Total length 3770'

Alternative (A2). Abutment towers, Tenderer's own design, granite facing to plinth level, precast
concrete blocks above plinth level ... ... £4,233,105 : 4 : 7

Tender A3

5 Spans : 198' 7" C. to C. Piers
193' 7" C. to C. Bearings

117'

1650'

117'

178' 7" C. to C. Prs. along C.L.
I.G. 165' 0" C. to C. Brgs.
O.G. 180' 6" " " "

S. Spans

Total length 3770'

(A3) In accordance with Official Design, granite facing throughout ... ... £4,217,721 : 11 : 10

(A3) Alternative. In accordance with Official Design, but with towers of precast concrete blocks above
plinth level ... ... £3,977,721 : 11 : 10

While families whose houses were demolished got no compensation, the Presbyterian Church fared much better. The historic Scots Church was demolished but the government gave it a new site at the corner of Margaret and York Streets.

Resumptions of property began more than a decade before the Bridge was built.

Although the Bridge was officially called the Sydney Harbour Bridge, it was popularly called, "The North Shore Bridge" by Sydney residents.

Residents gather on Milsons Point railway station, North Sydney to watch the opening procession.

The Bridge took eight years to build from start of evacuations in January 1925. The Opera House took ten years.

The Bridge is close to the deepest part of the harbour (off McMahon's Point).

WEAR A CHIP FROM THE

Sydney Harbour Bridge

The Latest Craze
Granite from the
Pylons of the Bridge
polished and mount-
ed in antique silver.

A Certificate from
Dorman Long & Co.
with each ring.

9/6 each

F. S. Burford & Son

JEWELLERS.
112 MARKET STREET, SYDNEY.

Two hundred stone masons were brought over from Scotland to build the Bridge. A special town was built to house them near the quarries at Moruya.

One of the many items of Bridge souvenir merchandise advertised in the 1930s featured a marble chip from the quarries.

The car ferry, *Kalang*, famous before the Bridge was built, later became The Sydney Show Boat and was eventually wrecked at Trial Bay while being towed to Japan for scrap.

Wreck of the car ferry Kalang; *she had originally come to Australia under her own steam.*

One of the reasons pylons were added to the Bridge was
that the public might think that the structure was unstable
without them.

In 1930 most of Sydney's tallest buildings would have fitted under the roadway.

H.M.A.S. CANBERRA.

Among those who thwarted the building of the Bridge for many decades were the Sydney ferry owners. Even by 1890 Sydney ferries carried five million passengers a year and by 1927 they carried 50 million.

Considering the sheer amount of ferry traffic on the harbour, there have been remarkably few serious accidents in the past century.

There was always controversy about who actually designed the Bridge – Bradfield or Ralph Freeman, the British consulting engineer to Dorman Long, the builders. In 1932 Dorman Long threatened to sue the New South Wales Government if it erected a plaque naming Bradfield as the designer. Much of the detailed design was entrusted to Lawrence Ennis but certainly Bradfield was really "the Father of the Bridge".

The very carefully worded plaque used to be out of sight (see arrow above) but in recent years it has resided in a more readable position on the northern pylon base.

SYDNEY HARBOUR BRIDGE

THE BRIDGE WAS CONSTRUCTED FOR AND THE APPROACHES BY THE
PUBLIC WORKS DEPARTMENT OF NEW SOUTH WALES.
THE GENERAL DESIGN AND SPECIFICATION WERE PREPARED AND
THE WHOLE SUPERVISED ON BEHALF OF THE GOVERNMENT OF NEW SOUTH WALES BY
J.J.C. BRADFIELD. D.SC.(ENG.). M.E. M.INST.C.E.. M.I.E. AUST.. CHIEF ENGINEER.

CONTRACTORS FOR THE DESIGN AND CONSTRUCTION OF THE MAIN STRUCTURE.
DORMAN, LONG AND CO. LIMITED. MIDDLESBROUGH. ENGLAND.
LAWRENCE ENNIS. O.B.E. DIRECTOR OF CONSTRUCTION FOR THE CONTRACTORS.
RALPH FREEMAN. M.INST.C.E.. M.AM.SOC.C.E..
CONSULTING AND DESIGNING ENGINEER FOR THE CONTRACTORS.
SIR JOHN BURNET AND PARTNERS. ARCHITECTS FOR THE CONTRACTORS.

THE HONOURABLE M.A.DAVIDSON. M.L.A.   G.W.MITCHELL.
MINISTER FOR PUBLIC WORKS.   DIRECTOR OF PUBLIC WORKS.

Photo opportunity: Dr Bradfield and party prepare to take a demonstration drive for the Press.

When the Bridge was built only a small percentage of Australians owned a car. Many thought the structure was preposterously large for its task.

The Bridge expands, rising and falling about 18 centimetres with fluctuations in temperature. The heat of the sun on one side of the bridge is enough to make it longer than the shaded side.

In the 1930s seaplanes were seen as the way of the future – now they are something of an oddity.

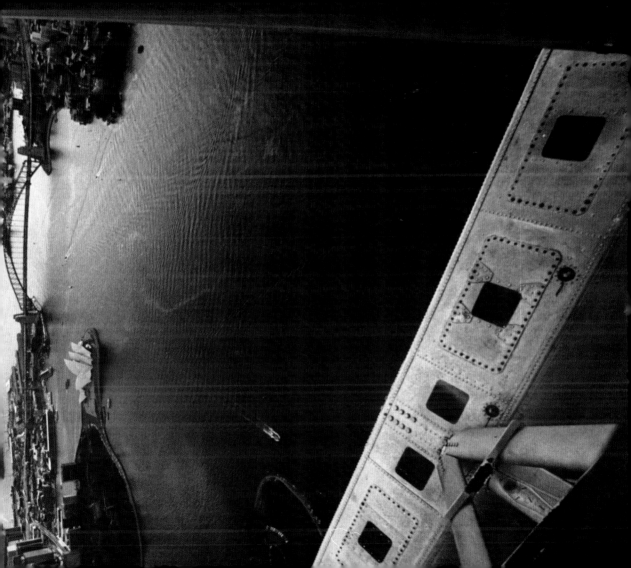

Architect John Sulman, who gave his name to the Sulman Prize, opposed the Bridge on the grounds that it was too large. The Bridge towered over the city which then had a height limit of 45 metres (150 feet) for all buildings.

Despite having been built three quarters of a century ago, the Bridge is still the dominant landmark in one of the world's great cities.

The newspaper *Smith's Weekly* forecast that someone would cut the ribbon before the official opening by the premier, Jack Lang.

New South Wales premier, Jack Lang, cuts the ribbon—watched by his nemesis, the governor Sir Phillip Game.

The famous Pylon Lookout was closed in 1942 to make way for anti-aircraft guns.

The pylons offer many tantalising glimpses of the harbour and its treasures.

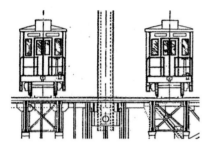

Trams used to run on the eastern side of the Bridge until 1959.

Double-decker buses, Buicks, Morrises, Austins, V8 Pilots and trams –
Sydney's traffic has changed almost as much as the city itself.

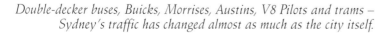

The Bridge rises 134 metres above sea level – almost the same height as The Great Pyramid at Giza in Egypt.

The Bridge weighs almost 40,000 tonnes. The Pyramid weighs 5.7 million tonnes.

The Harbour View Hotel was moved from the water's edge several hundred yards south and re-erected to make way for the Bridge.

Like a small museum, the historic Harbour View Hotel is full of Bridge memorabilia.

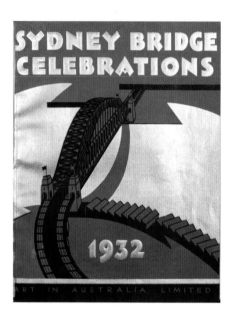

SYDNEY BRIDGE CELEBRATIONS

1932

ART IN AUSTRALIA LIMITED

Real estate agents, capitalising on the expected boom on the north shore, advertised blocks in Roseville, Pymble and Turramurra from 128 pounds, about $256.

Five quid deposit and ten bob a week – the average price for a property in these areas is now well over a million dollars!

The flat toll for each type of vehicle regardless of passengers was introduced in 1960.

Democracy at work – cars, buses, trucks and motor bikes jostle for position at the southern toll gates.

The Bridge has more than 100 moving parts including sliding bearings.

During construction the Bridge was momentarily hinged at the top of the arch and at the bases on either side of the harbour.

It would be 1959 before the number of private vehicles accounted for more passenger trips over the bridge than public transport.

One of Australia's best known and durable advertising campaigns: "It's Moments Like These ..."

It was expected that the Bridge would be paid for by 1980 but the Labor government added on four million dollars for the Cahill Expressway costs to the Bridge loan.

Beneath this vista a tunnel now runs to ease the bridge's traffic burden.

Because of the austerity of the Depression, the
government planned to have no fireworks or banquets
to commemorate the opening but later relented.
Thousands of school children made up this tableau on the
Sydney Cricket Ground.

John Allcott, (1888-1973), The Opening of the Sydney Harbour Bridge
1932, Oil on board. 45X50 cm. The pilot boat Captain Cook *leads the
procession of vessels under the Bridge. Following* Captain Cook *is the P&O
liner* Maloja *followed by the Orient liner* Orford *with the Dutch liner*
Nieweland *behind the southern pylon. Courtesy Roy Williams.*

Nearly all of the steel workers on the Bridge were fired in 1931. Many didn't work again until the 1940s.

Workers, friends and families were among the opening day throng.

The complete cost of the Bridge with loan interest was almost ten million pounds but even by January 1934 less than 15,000 pounds ($30,000) was taken in tolls. That's why it took most of the century to pay off the loan.

The Bridge, like its neighbour Luna Park, has weathered good times and bad times.

Some tall ships entering Sydney Harbour still had to lower their top masts to pass underneath the deck of the Bridge, as clearance is 53 metres at mean sea level.

The Pamir (right) didn't fit under the Bridge without some surgery to her rigging, and even the replica of the 16th century ship Batavia (above) had to wait until low tide to sneak under.

The Bridge's most famous rigger was Paul Hogan (right) who, after winning a talent quest in the 1970s, went on to become a comedian and actor.

G'day!

Sydney Harbour Bridge: Span 503 metres (1650 feet) pylon to pylon. Height 134 metres (440 feet). Weight including approaches 52,800 tonnes (51,996 tons). Span 39,000 tonnes. Opened March 19, 1932.
Titanic: 269metres (882 feet) (46,328 tonnes). Passengers 1316, crew 891. *Titanic* set sail on maiden voyage April 1, 1912. Sank April 14, 1912.

How the Titanic would have compared in size with the Sydney Harbour Bridge.

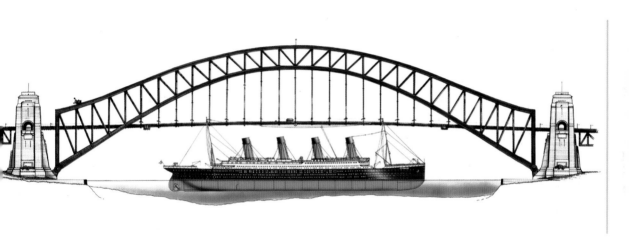

After the famous ribbon-cutting incident premier Jack Lang wanted
Captain de Groot committed to an asylum but a judge refused to find him
insane and fined him five pounds for disorderly behaviour.

*"He is not insane" ... a cigarette case memento showing that the crypto-Fascist New Guard
had dedicated supporters as well as enemies.*

In 1932, 4,500 pedestrians crossed the Bridge each day. Initially, it was planned that they would pay a toll but Jack Lang announced before the Bridge opened that pedestrians were toll-free. Even when the bridge had been opened for two years it carried less than a thousand vehicles a day.

If you look carefully at this diagram you can see the Bridge designers even catered for dog traffic.

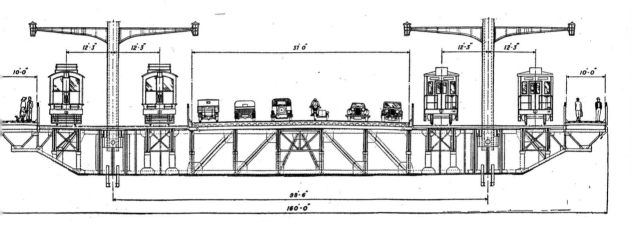

The Bridge has inspired creations in all disciplines – literature, theatre, film, music but particularly in the visual arts. Some of these works such as Dorrit Black's *The Bridge* (above) and Grace Cossington Smith's *The Bridge in Curve* (right) have become extremely valuable. The Cossington-Smith sold at auction in 2003 for $540,000. It was a new record for an Australian woman artist.

Painting 1(above): Dorrit Black (1891-1951) The Bridge *(c.1930). Oil on cardboard. Art Gallery of South Australia.*

Painting 2(right): Grace Cossington Smith(1892-1984), The Bridge in Curve *1926, Tempera on composition board. National Gallery of Victoria.*

Australia's most popular poet of the day, C.J. Dennis, was commissioned by Berger Paints to write an ode called "I dips me lid to The Sydney Harbour Bridge" to celebrate the opening.

> It 'appened this way: I 'ad jist come down,
> After long years, to look at Sydney town,
> An' 'struth! Was I knocked sideways? Fair su'prised?
> I never dreamed! That arch that cut the skies!
> The Bridge! I never thort there could 'a' been.

Magnificent Obsession

Who better to chronicle the life of the Bridge than Peter Luck, who's spent much of his 40 years in the media exploring the history of Australia's icons?

Peter has produced or presented most of Australia's major current affairs programs including *This Day Tonight*, *Four Corners*, *Sunday*, *Inside Edition*, *Hinch* and *Today Tonight*, along with his television series *This Fabulous Century*, *The Australians* and *Where Are They Now?* and has also made numerous short films and TV reports about the Sydney Harbour Bridge and the people whose lives it has touched.

The majority of pictures in this book have been supplied by the Peter Luck Productions Photo Library. As well, the publishers wish to thank and credit the following institutions and owners for reproduction of their material. Every care has been taken to trace copyright holders. However, if there are any omissions we will be happy to rectify them in future editions.

Fairfaxphotos pages 9, 11, 12, 15, 29, 42, 45, 49, 53, 55, 61, 63, 65, 67, 69, 72, 75, 80, 81, 89, 95, 104, 105, 106, 109, 111, 115, 119, 127, 130, 143, 148; State Records NSW pages 14, 20, 32, 34, 35, 36, 43, 44, 57, 60, 78, 92, 93, 96, 99, 100, 108, 123; FilmWorld pages 28, 134; Properties & Premises page 125; Archives Office of NSW page 30; Dorman Long & Co Ltd pages 90, 91, 148, 149; A.M. Annand page 83; Nestle Allen page 131; Mitchell Library NSW 147; Art Gallery of NSW page 87; National Gallery of Victoria page 151; Art Gallery of South Australia page 150; Berger Paints page 152; ScreenSound page 153; Roy Williams page 135

First published in Australia in 2006 by
New Holland Publishers (Australia) Pty Ltd
Sydney • Auckland • London • Cape Town

14 Aquatic Drive Frenchs Forest NSW 2086 Australia
218 Lake Road Northcote Auckland New Zealand
86 Edgware Road London W2 2EA United Kingdom
80 McKenzie Street Cape Town 8001 South Africa

10 9 8 7 6 5 4 3 2 1
National Library of Australia Cataloguing-in-Publication Data:

Luck, Peter, 1944- .
            Fascinating facts about the Sydney Harbour Bridge.

            ISBN(10) 1 74110 297 9
            ISBN(13) 978 1741102970

            1. Sydney Harbour Bridge (Sydney, N.S.W.) - History. 2.
            Sydney Harbour Bridge (Sydney, N.S.W.) - Pictorial works.
            I. Title.

            388.132099441

Publisher: Fiona Schultz
Editor: Martin Ford
Designer: Christina Macinerny
Printer: Leefung

Cover photo: Front: State Records NSW.
            Back: PLP Photo Library, Fairfaxphotos.

160